MY bed can be an aeroplane
Soaring through the sky.
Somersaulting, looping the loop
See me way up high.

My bed can be a jingling sleigh
Dashing through the snow.
Travelling to far off lands
As fast as it can go.

My bed can be a submarine,
Exploring beneath the sea.
Crabs and fish and mermaids
Smile and wave at me.

My bed can be a spaceship.
Flying through the stars.
Seeing comets, moons and meteors,
Or, even little men from Mars.

My bed is where I play my games,
And I'm sure you will agree,
It's really quite amazing
All the things a bed can be.

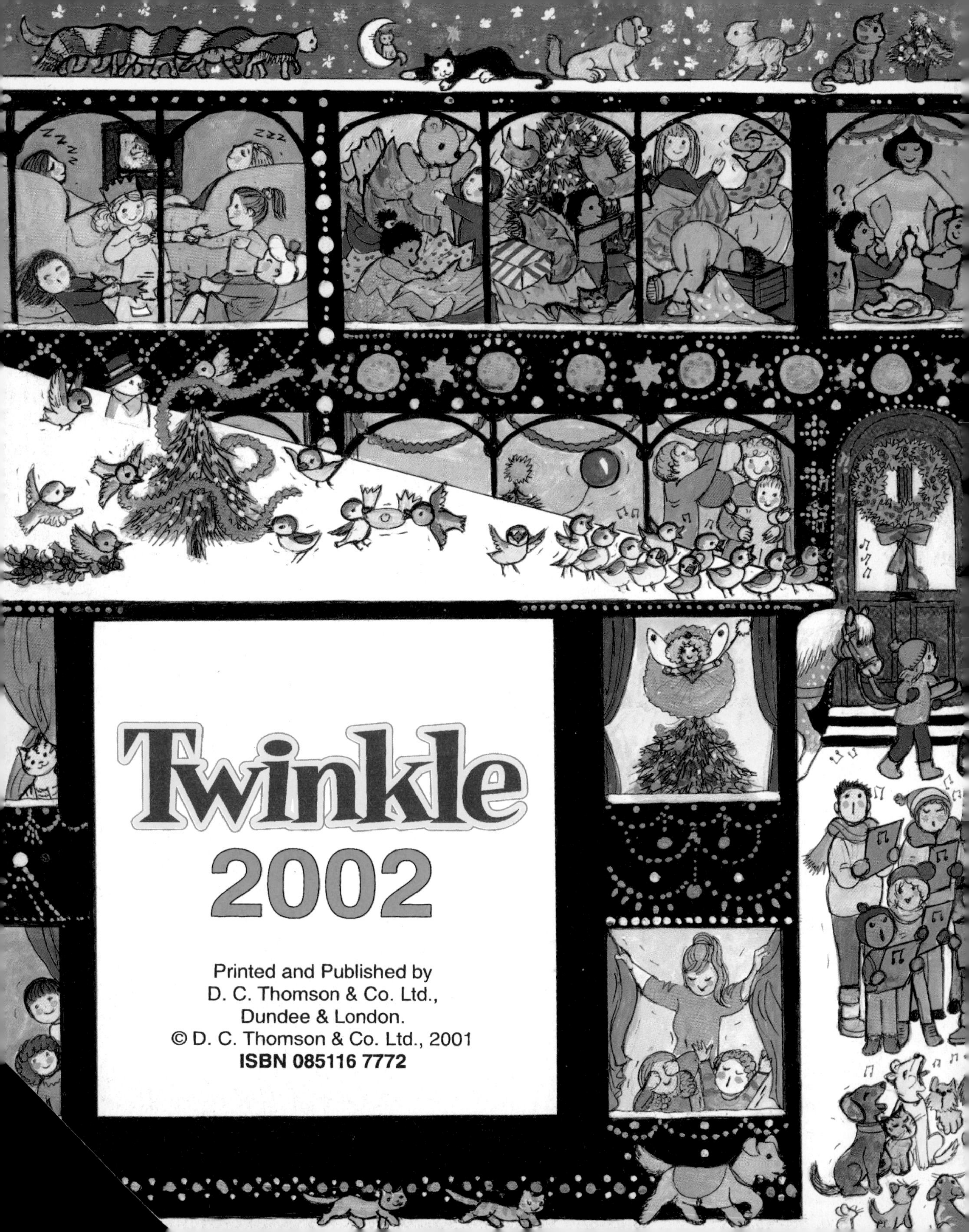

Twinkle 2002

Printed and Published by
D. C. Thomson & Co. Ltd.,
Dundee & London.

ISBN 085116 7772

Hello, everyone!
You'll have fun reading Twinkle 2002. Lots of favourites are here, including Silly Milly, The Blobs, Nurse Nancy and Patch, plus super stories — The Sad Tooth Fairy, A Great Adventure and The Magic Slippers. There are great games, puzzles and things to do, too, making 64 colourful pages specially for you!
Love,

Twinkle

Nurse Nancy

1 — Susie Dixon had brought her teddy to the Dollies Hospital. "I hope you can patch his ear," she said anxiously. "Grandad might do it while you wait," smiled Nancy.

2 — Mr Jingle said it wouldn't take long to repair the teddy. While Susie waited, another girl arrived. "Hi, Titch!" she teased Susie. Nancy thought that was unkind.

3 — Later, Ryan and Clare Bentley arrived with a broken trampoline. "Bring it in then go into the waiting room," Nancy told them.

4 — "What are *you* doing here, Tiny?" asked Ryan when he saw Susie. But the little girl ignored the taunt.

5 — After the trampoline had been repaired, Nancy helped her grandad put it in the garden. "Perhaps the children would like to try it," she said.

6 — Susie was very keen to try out the trampoline. Ryan laughed but said she could have a go. "I can't wait to see this," he grinned as Susie hurried outside.

7 — But Ryan was in for a shock, as were the other children. It turned out that Susie was an expert on the trampoline. "They won't laugh at her now," smiled Nancy. "Susie's higher than all of them, now!"

The Blobs

...bright little blobs of paint who come out of a paintbox into the wonderful world of Paintbox Land.

Royal Blue and the parade

The Blobs were very excited. There was to be a Grand Parade through Paintbox Land and the Blobs were waiting for King Royal Blue to arrive in his royal coach.

They waited and waited . . . and waited.

Finally, Poppy Red went to see what was holding up the king. She found Royal Blue sitting beside his coach looking very miserable.

"I've cancelled the parade," said the king with a sigh. "My royal coach is so old and dull, I'm ashamed to be seen riding in it any more."

"I see," said Poppy Red.

Poppy hurried back to tell her friends.

"Why don't we paint the royal coach?" suggested Primrose Yellow. "A yellow coach would look very nice."

"No, I think it should be green," said Grumbly Green.

"What's wrong with orange?" said Fizzy Orange.

The chums started arguing about the colour of the coach until Rainbow Blob stepped forward. He had a plan.

Soon after, the Blobs arrived back with lots of different colours of paint and started work on Royal Blue's boring old coach. They used RED, ORANGE, YELLOW, GREEN, BLUE, INDIGO, and VIOLET.

When they had finished, Royal Blue climbed aboard his shining new coach.

"Thank you," he said smiling gratefully to the chums.

The Grand Parade was able to go ahead after all and everyone had a wonderful time — especially Royal Blue in his bright, new, rainbow coach!

fun to colour

THE MAGIC SLIPPERS

MADELEINE didn't know that her new mouse slippers were magic. She knew that they were special, because they were so cute with their soft brown fur and lovely pink noses.

Every night, Madeleine placed them under her bed. And, as soon as everyone was asleep, the little pink noses would twitch then each little slipper would slip out from beneath the bed.

2 — Very quietly, they'd shuffle across the bedroom floor, flip-flop, flip-flop then quickly down the stairs.

But now they looked more like *real* mice. Noses quivering, they would creep round the sitting room door and, with a very loud *squeak,* wake up the toys in the toy box.

"Silly slippers!" the dolls would complain. "Why can't they play outside?"

3 — But the mouse slippers loved teasing the toys. They patted the balls and scattered the bricks until eventually, tired out, they would fall asleep.

Madeleine's mummy would appear in the morning and see toys all over the floor, with Madeleine's slippers lying in the middle of them.

"Madeleine!" she would call. "Have you been down here?"

"No, I haven't," Madeleine would tell her.

But she could never explain why her slippers were lying with the toys.

4 — Then one wintry evening, the slippers hurried down the stairs and across the chilly hall.

"Squeak," they cried as they jumped into the warm sitting room.

But there they stopped, because, slowly uncurling itself on the hearthrug, was a little grey kitten.

The mouse slippers turned to run but, quick as a flash, the kitten caught them. It patted them all around the sitting room just as the slippers had done with Madeleine's toys, until, eventually, tired out, it curled up to sleep in front of the fire.

5 — The frightened slippers crept back up to Madeleine's bedroom where they would have stayed forever had they not had a surprise visitor one evening.

As they played quietly in the bedroom, the door opened and a little pink nose pushed its way in. It was the *kitten!*

The mouse slippers scurried under the bed, but the kitten didn't chase them.

He miaowed softly.

"Please play with me," he purred. "I get so lonely when Madeleine goes to bed at night."

6 — And so, every night after that, the slippers played with the grey kitten.

They never teased the toys again, remembering how frightened *they* were when the kitten played roughly with them.

Then, when they were tired out, they would climb upstairs to Madeleine's bedroom.

The little girl couldn't figure out why her slippers were always under her bed in the mornings now. And they were never alone — there were always *three* little pink noses snuggled together!

Woodland Wonders

Which route must the little harvest mouse take to get back down to earth?

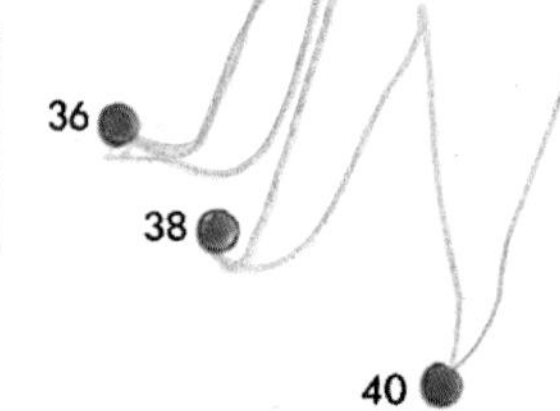

Join the dots to find one of our larger feathered friends.

ANSWERS
JOIN THE DOTS — Eagle
HARVEST MOUSE — Route 2
OWL'S NAME — Barnaby
LOST MOUSE — Route D

Find the owl's name from these jumbled letters:
ANBRBYA
Which of the four routes must the mouse take to join his friends? He must not cross a black line.
A
B
C
D

Silly Milly

1 — When Milly went on a skiing trip, she found she could hardly move in her padded skiing suit. "And these silly boots are too difficult to walk in," she grumbled as she lost her balance in the snow.

3 — At last, Milly made it to the higher slopes and soon, she was having great fun. "This is *brilliant*," she yelled excitedly as she zoomed downhill towards everyone. Then, suddenly, she shrieked, "How do I stop?"

2 — Milly struggled to her feet on the slippery slope and set off to the ski lift. She annoyed the other skiers when she couldn't get on. "Hurry up, you silly girl!" they cried angrily. "We'll *never* get to the top."

4 — Milly crashed into the others, scattering them in all directions. They *were* annoyed. Milly was quite pleased, however. "Now I see why ski clothes are so padded," she said with a grin. "That didn't hurt one bit!"

Can you find 15 snowballs?

Snowy Day Fun

SNOWY days are just the best,
There's lots and lots to do . . .
Skiing, sledging, snowball fights
And building snowmen too!

Out on the snow-white slopes we go,
To laugh, and shout, and cheer.
Oh, friends can have such *brilliant* fun
When wintertime is here.

Marmalade

1 — One day, Marmalade the cat watched Annie and Steven's dad take a taxi to work. "Bye, Dad!" the children called.

2 — "That gives me an idea for a game," said Steven. Marmalade hoped it wasn't a noisy game. He *hated* noisy games!

3 — Annie put a soft cushion on the basket of Steven's trike. "Jump on Marmalade!" she cried. "We're playing taxis!" laughed Steven. Marmalade purred happily. He liked *this* game!

Fairy Fay

1 — Fairy Fay and Fairy Lavender didn't know what to do. The fairy babies were being very badly behaved. "It's not their fault. They need toys to play with," said Fay. "They're just feeling bored."

2 — "Let's see if we can find some toys," Fay went on. Fairy Cowslip stayed behind to look after the babies. "Don't be long," she called as Fay and Lavender flew off.

3 — In the village, there was a wonderful toy shop. Fay and Lavender looked longingly in the window. "There are some lovely toys," said Fay, "but they're *human* children's toys — far too big for fairy babies."

4 — "We don't have money to buy anything, anyway," Lavender said. "We'll have to think of another idea." Then as the fairies flew over the park, Fay spotted something on the ground. "What's that down there?" she asked.

5 — Fay and Lavender fluttered down to have a closer look. It was a paper bag of jelly babies that someone had dropped. "Help me pick it up," Fay said to Lavender excitedly. "I know what we can do with these." And the two fairies struggled to carry the bag of sweets back to the glade. "Ooh! This bag is heavy," groaned Lavender.

6 — But it was worth the effort, however. "We've got dolls for you all," called Fairy Fay. The fairy babies loved the *jelly babies* and there were no more naughty children as they played happily all day.

DEBBIE is a pretty little girl who likes to dress up. One day, however, she was ill and had to stay in bed.

"I'm so bored lying here," grumbled Debbie. "I can't even dress up!"

Just then, Debbie's Grandma arrived with a basket full of goodies. There was a story book, a new doll, fruit and a jig-saw.

"Ooh! Thank you!" cried Debbie.

Debbie wasn't bored anymore. Grandma helped her with the jig-saw and then read stories from the book.

Finally, Debbie snuggled down with her new doll. When she was sleeping soundly, Grandma set off home.

2 — Debbie soon began to feel *much* better. Within a few days, she was up and about again. However, now *Grandma* wasn't well.

"Let's visit her," said Debbie. "I can cheer her up, just like *she* did for me."

As Mummy gathered some things to take with them, Debbie ran upstairs to change into a Red Riding Hood outfit.

"Grandma will feel better once she sees our presents," smiled Debbie.

"Yes," laughed Mummy. "I just hope we don't meet the big bad wolf on the way!"

3 — "Try to be useful and look for the postman," grumbled Wendy as she began clearing up the mess on the floor.

4 — A little later, the postman appeared. He trudged wearily up the snow-covered path with a very heavy sack of Christmas mail. "I'm never going to finish my round today," he groaned.

5 — "Please, Mr Postman, let me help you," said Winkle fetching her broomstick. "I know how to deliver the post on time *and* it will give me something to do."

6 — And so, off they flew, high above the roofs and streets of the town. "This is great!" cried the happy postman. "No slippy pavements or snowdrifts for me!"

LOST KITTENS GAME
START
1
2
3
Chased by a dog. Move on 3 squares.
4
5
Frightened to cross a busy road. Miss a turn.
6
7
8
Stop to enjoy some milk. Miss a turn.
9
10
Caught in a downpour. Throw a 6 to move on.
11
Ride in a shopping trolley. Move on 2 squares.
12
Lick butter from paws. Miss a turn.
13
14
Make a donation to the Cats' Home. Move on to 19.
15
CORN FLAKES
Pay Cats Home
£5

lp the kittens find their way
me by playing this fun game.
l you need is a dice and
unters. Each player must throw
ix to start and the first one
me is the winner.
FINISH
Flap
30
The cat flap is jammed. Go back 3 squares.
FISH
29
28
Fall in a garden pond. Miss a turn.
27
Take a wrong turning and go back to 23.
26
STOP
25
21
20
Stuck in a tree. Miss a turn.
22
Helped by a lollipop lady. Cross over to 25.
24
23
18
19
A bike ride takes you on to 21.
16
Tangled in wool. Go back to 15.
17

My Baby Brother

"NOW it's December, Ben," I said.
"The last month of the year.
Quite soon it will be Christmas Day!"
And Benny gave a cheer.

Out in the kitchen, Mummy said,
"Time to make a Christmas pud!"
I made a wish, Ben gave a stir,
And, ooh, it did smell good!

Mum filled the basin with the mix,
But she was left with some.
I found a little bowl, and asked,
"Please may I have that, Mum?"

Into the bowl I piled the mix,
And tied it neatly then.
"There! Our very special pud!"
I said to little Ben.

BERTIE

1 — Hi! I'm Bertie and I'm off to play with Andrew in the park.

2 — Oh-oh! Where's young Andrew run off to?

3 — He wasn't on the roundabout. Oh! I'm dizzy!

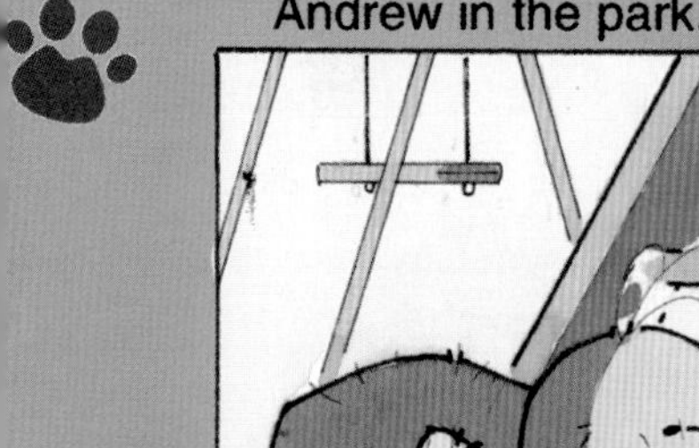

4 — I think he climbed up these steps. I'll do the same. I wonder where they lead to?

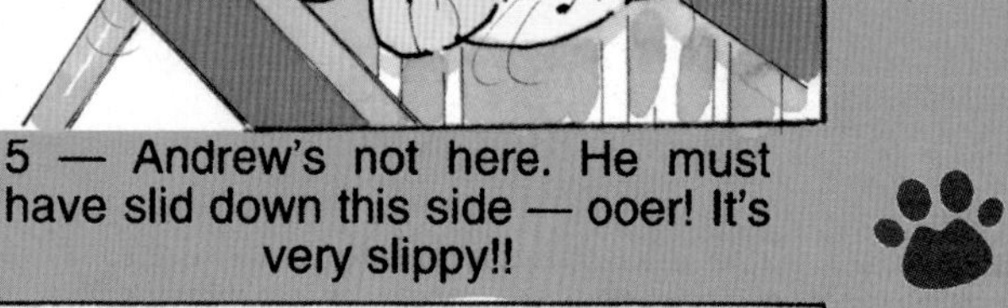

5 — Andrew's not here. He must have slid down this side — ooer! It's very slippy!!

6 — I'm going much too fast. I can't stop! I'll fall off the end! Help me, someone!

7 — Oh, good! Someone's waiting at the bottom to catch me! It's Andrew! Hooray!

Polly

1 — Polly Penguin lives in Snowland with her chums, Suki Seal, Peter Polar Bear and Rodney Reindeer. One bright morning, the friends decided to try skiing on a nearby hill.

2 — Polly and her friends hadn't played very long, before all the skis and poles they had were broken into pieces. "We weren't much good at *that,*" sighed Polly holding up a broken ski.

3 — "I really wanted to slide all the way down the hill on that lovely white snow," Polly continued. Peter, Rodney and Suki nodded their heads in agreement. Then Rodney had an idea.

4 — "Come with me!" he told the chums. "I wonder where he is going?" said Polly. Peter and Suki had no idea either but they all decided to follow Rodney anyway. Very soon, he led them to Santa Claus's house.

5 — “Wait here,” said Rodney as he hurried inside. A few minutes later, he appeared again, pulling something covered by a large blanket. “Come on!” he called to the others. “Lend a hand!” The chums *were* puzzled.

6 — So they all began pushing the object uphill. “What have you got hidden under this blanket?“ grumbled Suki with a puff and a pant. “It’s very, *very* heavy.” “You’ll find out soon enough,” laughed Peter.

7 — After much pulling and pushing, they finally reached the top of the hill. Rodney pulled off the blanket to reveal a *big* surprise. “It’s Santa’s sleigh!” cried Peter. “When I told Santa about our skis, he said we could borrow it,” explained Rodney. Polly and her friends *did* have fun.

fun to colour

The Sad Tooth Fairy

FLOSS, the smallest tooth fairy, was very excited. Tonight was to be her first night delivering the silver coins on her own.

The Fairy Queen handed Floss a small bag of silver coins. "Be careful," she warned. "Take care not to be seen. Children are usually kind, but they may hurt you without meaning to, if they catch you."

Fairy Floss flew off to the first house on her list. The window was slightly open and the little fairy slipped inside.

She landed lightly on the top bunk of a bunk bed where a little girl lay sleeping. Then, very gently, she slid one of the silver coins under the pillow.

2 — Floss turned to go — but something was stopping her.

A girl's voice rang out. "I've got her! Emily! Wake up! I've caught the tooth fairy with my fishing net!"

"Oh, Lynsay, she's beautiful!" gasped Emily, Lynsay's sister.

"Please let me out!" cried Floss.

But the girls couldn't hear Floss's pleas. Her voice just made tinkling sounds to them.

"Let's keep her in the doll's house," Emily suggested and Lynsay agreed.

3 — Next morning, the girls brought a little thimbleful of cornflakes for Floss, but she was too homesick to eat anything.

Fairy Floss knew that her magic was running out. If fairies were away too long from Fairyland, their magic began to fade. Soon, Floss wouldn't be able to fly!

The little fairy also knew that the Fairy Queen would send out the Rescue Squad to search for her, but that wouldn't be till nightfall — and it was a long time till then!

4 — Emily and Lynsay heard Floss crying, but they thought she was singing.

"It sounds quite a sad song," sighed Emily in a worried voice.

"She's not as sparkly as she was," said Lynsay. "Perhaps she's not well."

They fetched a teaspoonful of honey but Fairy Floss took no notice of it.

"We must let her go," Emily and Lynsay decided sadly.

They opened the door of the doll's house, but Floss was too weak to fly away.

5 — That night, in bed, as the girls worried about Floss, there was a crackle like tiny fireworks and hundreds of little bright lights burst into the room.

"Your friends have come to take you home!" gasped Lynsay as the rescuers lifted Floss, in a hammock of silver cobwebs and carried her away into the night.

Floss soon recovered, but the Fairy Queen made a new rule, that tooth fairies must always work in pairs and carry an extra pouch of magic with them — just in case!

Puzzle time
Amy is going shopping with her family.
Join the dots to see which toy Joe hopes to find in his Christmas stocking.
Amy has found the dolls that she likes. Two of them are exactly the same. Can you spot them?
Amy wants to visit Santa in his grotto. Can you help her decide which path she should take to reach him?
While Amy and her family queue to see Santa, can you see six differences between this picture and the one at the top of the page?

At last, it's Amy's turn to meet Santa. Four of her friends are visiting him too. Can you see where they are in the big picture?

These are some of the toys Santa is giving away. Find where they are before you colour in the picture.

1 — "Oh, look at my new doll's house!" cried Nadia as her daddy added the finishing touches. "It's beautiful!" Nadia's pets, Cuddles the dog and Midge and Tiny the cats, watched carefully as Nadia's daddy glued on the last piece, the chimney. The dog and cats *were* impressed.

2 — Later, Cuddles, Midge and Tiny looked on as Nadia arranged some pieces of doll's furniture in the new house. "These little chairs are so cute," smiled Nadia. "Mummy said she would take me to the toy shop this afternoon, to buy more. The shop in town has a super selection of furniture."

— Nadia couldn't wait to go in ne shop. "I have some pocket noney to spend," she said. The pets pricked up their ears.

4 — Nadia chose a grandfather clock and a little bed. Then she spotted Cuddles, Midge and Tiny staring through the shop window.

5 — "My cheeky pets have spotted the pets for the doll's house," laughed Nadia. "I'll buy some with my change, just to please them." So, Nadia bought a kitten, dog and cat. Cuddles, Midge and Tiny *were* pleased.

6 — Back home, Nadia arranged ner new furniture in the doll's nouse. She sat the three toy pets by the fireside. "Just like you three on a cold winter's night," Nadia told her pets with a smile.

Nurse Nancy

1 — One very windy day, Nurse Nancy stopped to chat to Mr Owen who ran the local animal sanctuary. Mr Owen was busy repairing the damage to a fence. "It blew down during the night," he explained to Nancy. "I just hope that none of the animals escaped. They could have gone *anywhere* by now."

2 — Mr Owen showed Nancy inside the sanctuary. There were all types of animals there. "I'd better get back to my *own* patients, now," smiled Nancy later.

3 — At the Dollies Hospital, Nancy's grandad was struggling with a damaged fence, too. "I'll fix it later," said Mr Jingle. "I have patients to see."

4 — There were *lots* of patients and Nancy and Grandad were kept *very* busy. Nancy didn't see a little kitten creep through a gap in the fence. Then she heard a "miaow".

5 — "I wonder if you escaped from the sanctuary?" thought the little nurse. But when Nancy went round to see Mr Owen, the centre was closed.

6 — Nancy left a note for Mr Owen, then she took the kitten back to the hospital. She made a bed from a shoe box. "That will keep you cosy," she told the kitten as she gently tucked it in.

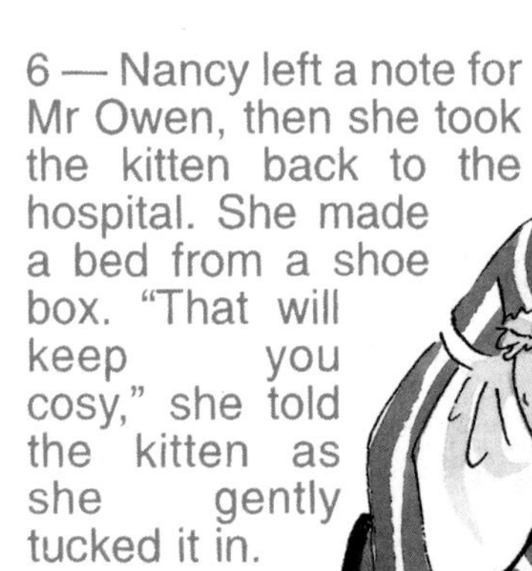

7 — When Mr Owen arrived at the Dollies Hospital next day, he recognised the kitten right away. "His name is Socks," he told Nancy. Mr Owen was so pleased that Socks was safe, he asked if he could do anything in return. "Well, you could fix Grandad's fence," said Nancy with a smile. "He hasn't had time."

Sally and Scamp

SALLY'S best friend is her cheeky Shetland pony called Scamp. He lives in a field next door to Sally's house and they have lots of fun together. Every night, after school, Sally feeds and exercises Scamp.

2 — One bright, winter's, afternoon, Sally's mum hurried outside to see her. "Come and see the newspaper!" she called to Sally. Puzzled Sally trotted Scamp over to Mum, wondering what had made her so excited.

3 — "Look at this!" said Mum pointing to a notice in the paper. It was advertising a fancy dress contest to be held in the village hall the weekend before Christmas. "Why don't *you* enter, Sally?" asked Mum. "It will be fun."

4 — Sally thought entering the competition was a super idea. But when she had a look in her dressing-up box, she *was* disappointed. "This is too small and that's not warm enough," she sighed. "I can't find *anything* to wear."

5 — Sally told Mum that she couldn't enter the competition because she didn't have a costume. "Why don't we make something *new.* It's nearly Christmas, so you can go as Santa Claus," said Mum. And that's what they did.

6 — Sally's costume was lovely and Scamp wasn't forgotten either. With a bright red nose and reindeer antlers, he became Rudolph! On the day of the fancy dress contest, Sally and Scamp won the prize for the most *unusual* costume.

Buttons

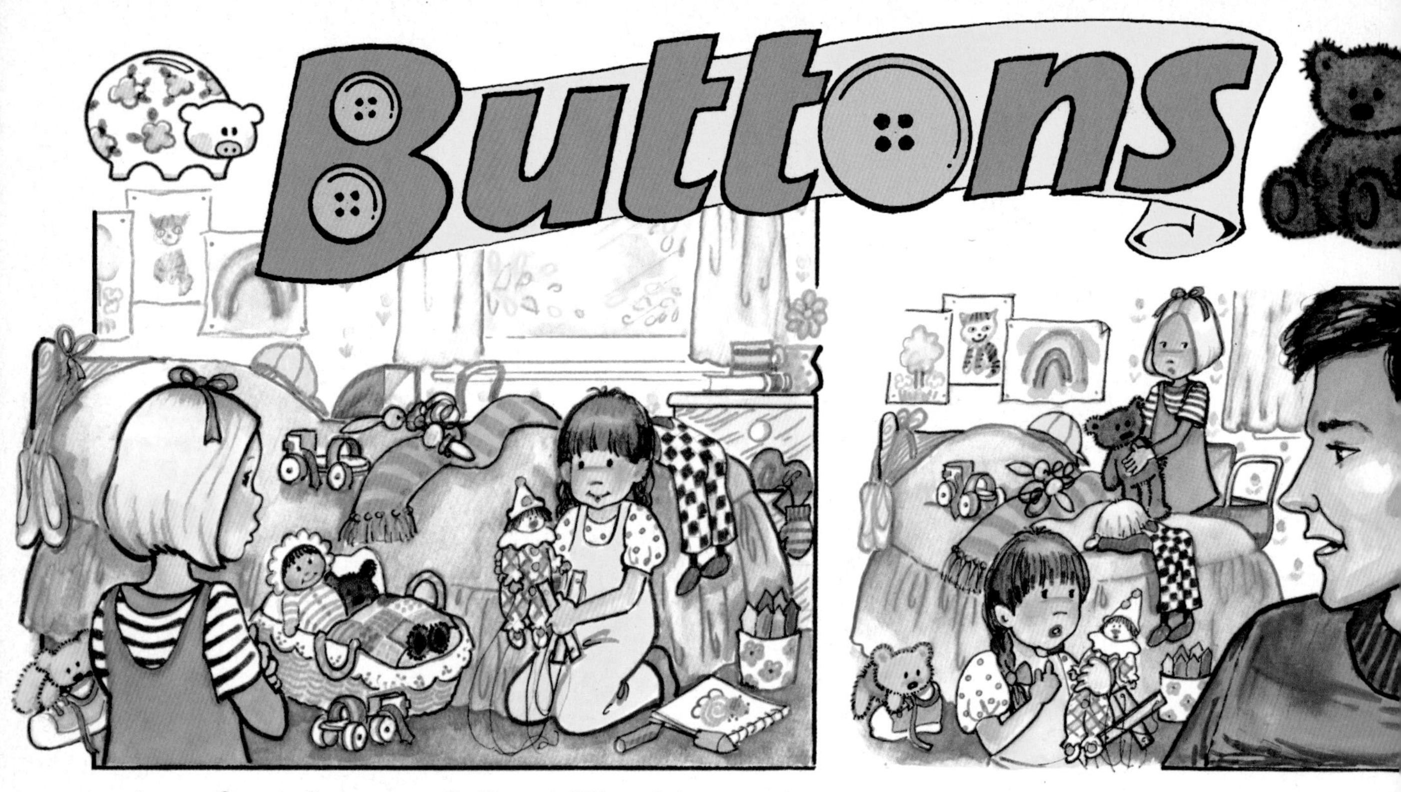

1 — One afternoon, Buttons' little sister was playing in her bedroom. The little girl had been having fun with the toys, paints and crayons, but now they were scattered all over the room.

2 — Just then, Daddy appeared When he saw the untidy room, he was angry. "Who made all this mess?" he asked. "*I* did," answered Zoe.

3 — Daddy told Zoe to put *all* the toys away. But when Buttons looked at the toy tidy, she saw that it was full and the toy boxes were full, too.

4 — "I don't know where to put these toys," sighed Zoe later. "*I* do!" cried Buttons. "These old coats are just what we need — you'll see!"

5 — Buttons was right! The two coats, with their huge pockets, made *perfect* toy tidies. Before long, Zoe and Buttons had picked up all the toys from the floor. "Daddy *was* pleased. "Well done, girls!" he told them afterwards.

How to make Paper Santas

All you have to do is trace the Santa picture on to a long strip of paper and fold as shown. Carefully cut round the shaded area. Now open out the paper and colour in your Santas.

A great adventure

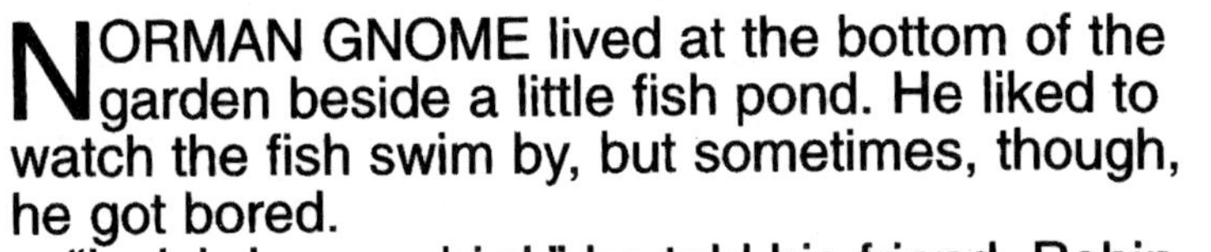

NORMAN GNOME lived at the bottom of the garden beside a little fish pond. He liked to watch the fish swim by, but sometimes, though, he got bored.

"I wish I was a bird," he told his friend, Robin, one day. "You can fly off and have lots of exciting adventures."

"It's not all fun being a bird," Robin chirped. "It can be lots of hard work, too, looking for food and building nests."

"Well, I think it would be wonderful," sighed Norman.

While Norman dreamed of being a bird soaring through the sky, Muffy the cat came along.

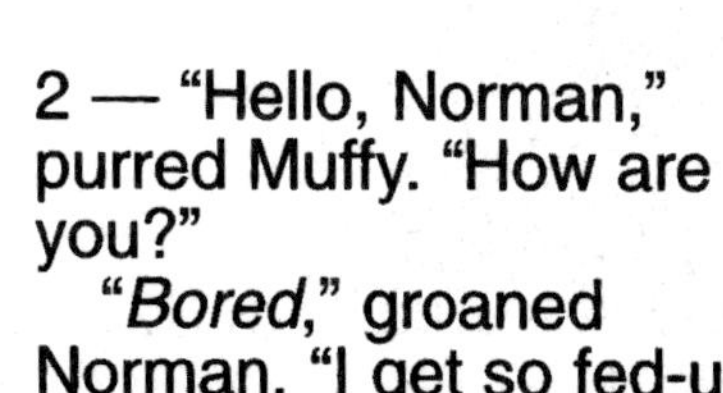

2 — "Hello, Norman," purred Muffy. "How are you?"

"*Bored*," groaned Norman. "I get so fed-up just sitting here. I wish I could go *somewhere*, do *something*!"

Norman looked at Muffy enviously and sighed.

"I wish I could be a cat, exploring the woods, going anywhere I wanted with a leap and a bound. Oh, I wish I could have a *great adventure* if only for just one day!"

3 — That night, Robin and Muffy gathered together some of the animals and birds who lived in the garden.

"It would be lovely to do something for Norman," Muffy told them. "He's such a nice fellow."

Ollie Owl suggested a flying trip.

"Get the other birds to help you," he told Robin. "Roll Norman into an empty nest and carry him into the air between you!"

4 — The others thought that Ollie's idea was perfect and, next day, Norman had some surprise visitors.

After much pushing and pulling, the little gnome was carefully rolled into the empty birds' nest by Robin and his friends.

With a flutter of wings, the nest rose higher and higher into the air. Norman could see the garden far below, and soon, he was flying over the forest and the snow-covered hills beyond.

To his amazement, Norman Gnome was having an exciting time, and, to be truthful, he was finding it a bit scary.

5 — A little later, the birds lowered Norman to the ground. His surprises didn't end there, however. Muffy was waiting for him to begin her part of the adventure.

The little cat was harnessed to the nest, and soon, Norman was speeding along the forest path.

"Isn't this fun?" cried Muffy.

But Norman couldn't answer. He could only grit his teeth as they whizzed past trees and bushes at an alarming rate.

6 — Later that afternoon, Norman was returned safely to the garden pond.

"Did you enjoy your adventures, Norman?" asked Muffy.

"Oh, yes," said Norman, for there was no way he would spoil the day by saying how absolutely *terrified* he had been.

The little gnome had had a great adventure, at last, but from now on, a visit from his very kind and thoughtful friends, Robin and Muffy, would be excitement enough.

Patch
1 — One warm, sunny summer's afternoon, Paula's kitten, Patch, was playing in the garden. Suddenly, he came running into the house looking scared. "Something's frightened Patch?" thought Paula. "I wonder what it is?"
2 — Paula decided to go into the garden to investigate. Patch went, too, tip-toeing warily behind her. "Oh, Patch," giggled Paula when she saw the "monster" that had scared him. "It's a little caterpillar!"

3 — Paula fetched the visitor a big, juicy leaf to eat. "This is a snack for the caterpillar," she explained. "Now *we'll* go in and have a snack, too!"

4 — A few weeks later, Paula and Patch spotted a beautiful, blue butterfly fluttering around the garden. "It's our caterpillar!" cried Paula excitedly.

5 — Patch wasn't sure how the caterpillar had become a butterfly, but he did have fun playing with it. "I think the butterfly is enjoying the game, too," said Paula as the little creature flitted just out of reach of the kitten's paws.

Puzzle Time

Jenni and her schoolchums are learning all about dragons.

Can you find the following words in the wordsearch?

DRAGON TAIL
CASTLE FLAG
FIRE TOWER
MOAT FEAR

Tonia has found cuddly toy dragons in the cupboard. Can you find two exactly the same?

Join the dots to see what Lesley is about to paint.

Can you spot six differences between these two dragons?

Welcome to the school play — all about castles, dragons and a princess trapped in a tower. It's so exciting!

Can you make up your own story about dragons then colour the picture with your paints or crayons?

Look at the small pictures. See if you can find where they fit in the big picture.

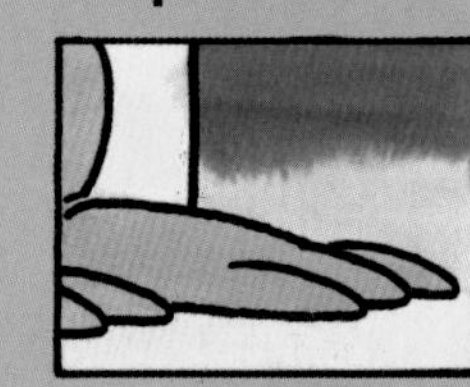

Find your way through the maze for a surprise!

I'M gazing at the night sky,
It looks so deep and black,
And a thousand twinkling stars
Look like they're staring back.

It seems like they are winking,
Perhaps they've jokes to tell,
Or secrets they are keeping
Of friends that rose and fell.

And now the moon moves slowly,
Like a dream across the night.
She's the princess of the evening,
In a glow of silver light.

I wish I could fly up
And explore among the stars,
See the golden rings of Saturn
Or the bright red glow of Mars.

I'm gazing at the night sky,
There is such a lot to see,
And maybe someone up there
Could be gazing down at me.